BODY INK ENVY

A MULTI-LEVEL CREATIVE COLOURING BOOK

Welcome to Body Ink Envy

This multi-level Creative Colouring Book

will engage you with irresistible designs ranging in complexity from beginner to challenging.
With plenty to discover, this interactive colouring book offers motifs to complete, mazes to solve
and spaces for you to add your own creative doodles and drawings.

As an added activity, hidden throughout the pages you can find these tiny silhouettes.

Good luck!

5 Moons   **3** Butterflies   **2** Sugar Skulls   **3** Dragonflies   **4** Scarabs

3 Dragons   **12** Rosebuds   **5** Suns   **5** Snakes   **8** Feathers

6 Hearts   **6** Hummingbirds   **5** Koi Fish   **2** Owls   **5** Lotus Flowers

Editorial and design team:
Bill Mersereau, Tammy Desnoyers, Doran Woo, Jennifer Barrett

This edition is exclusively published in the UK in 2023 by Alligator Products Ltd.
UK Address: 2nd Floor, 314 Regents Park Road, London N3 2JX.

EU Address: Calle Arquitecto Francisco Casas Nº 10
Apto. Sa Vinya T101, 07181 Bendinat - Calviá, Baleares - Spain

Printed in China. 2008

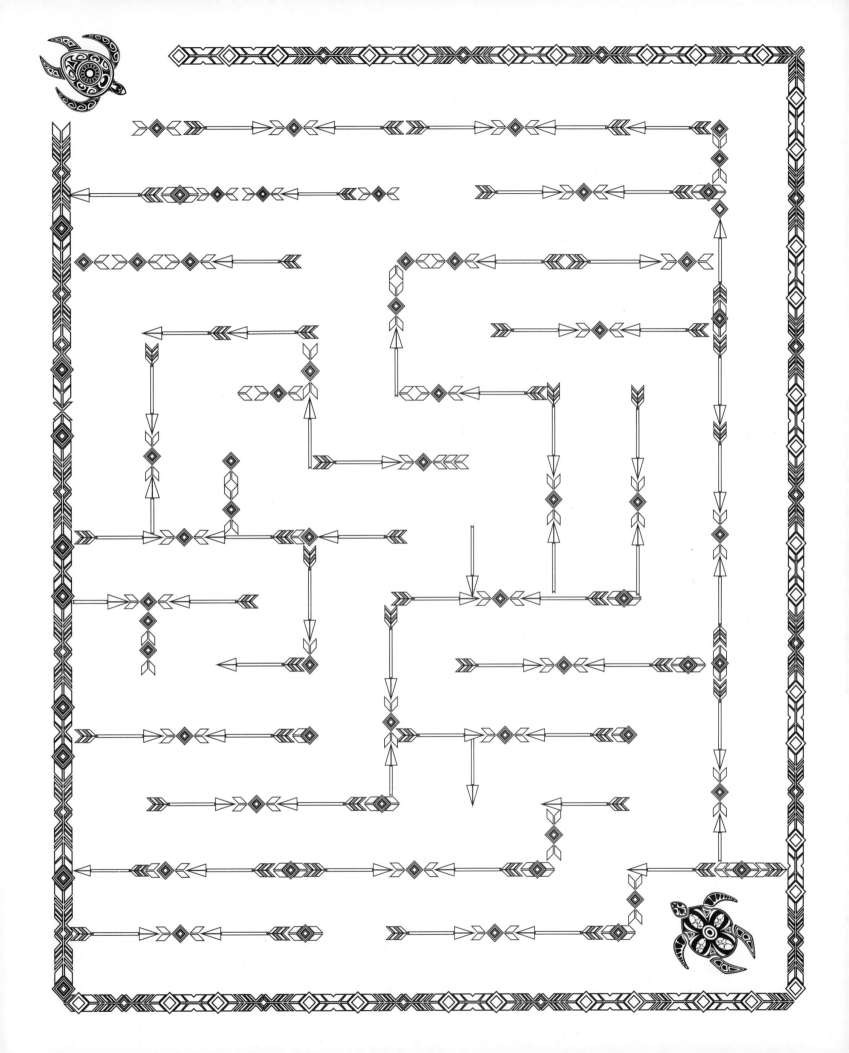

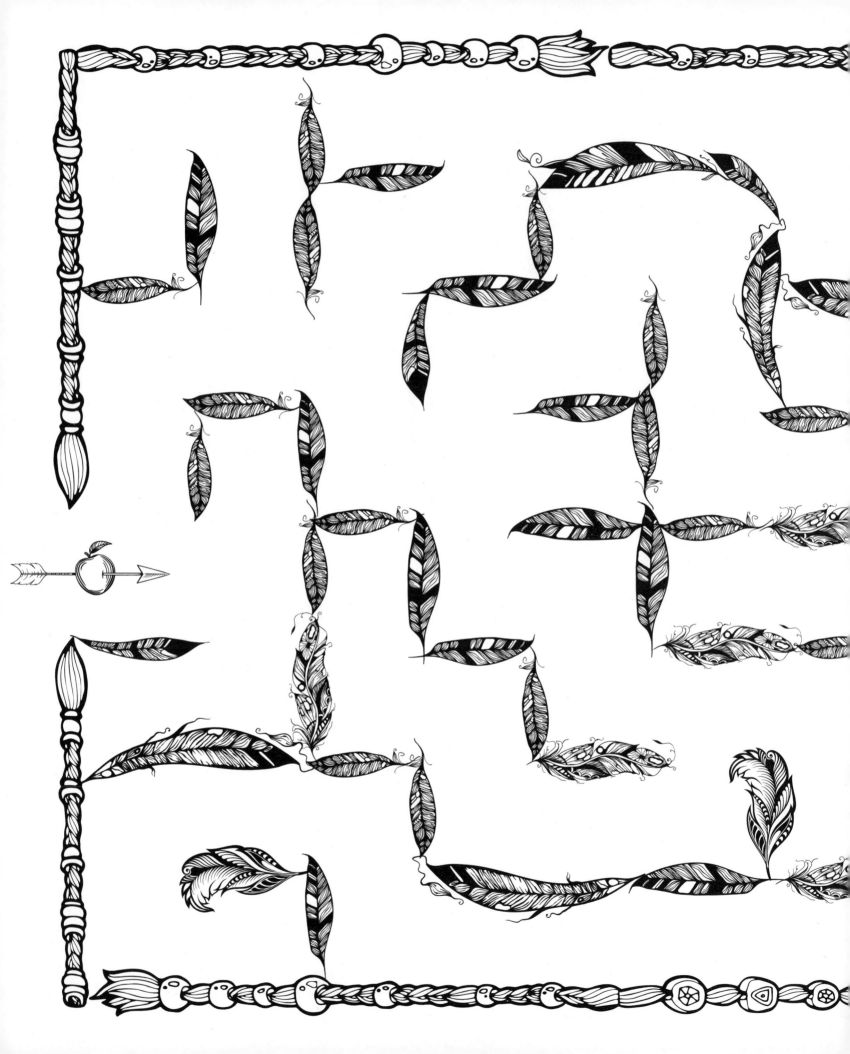

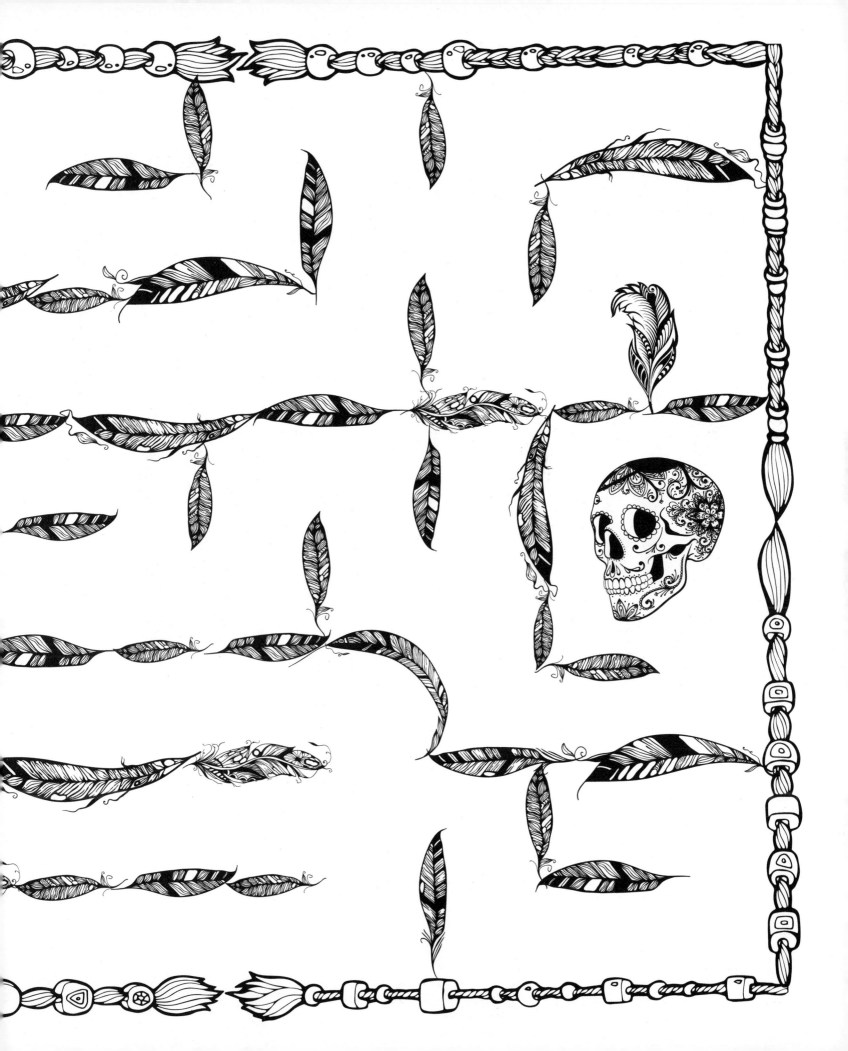

Larosa

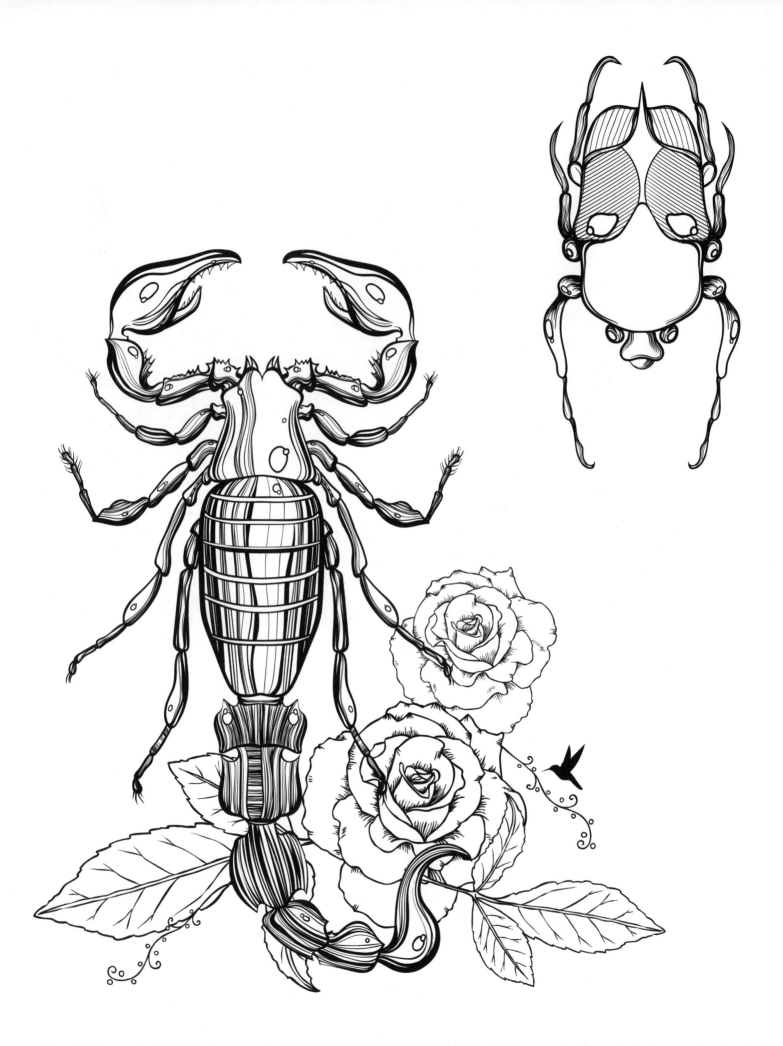

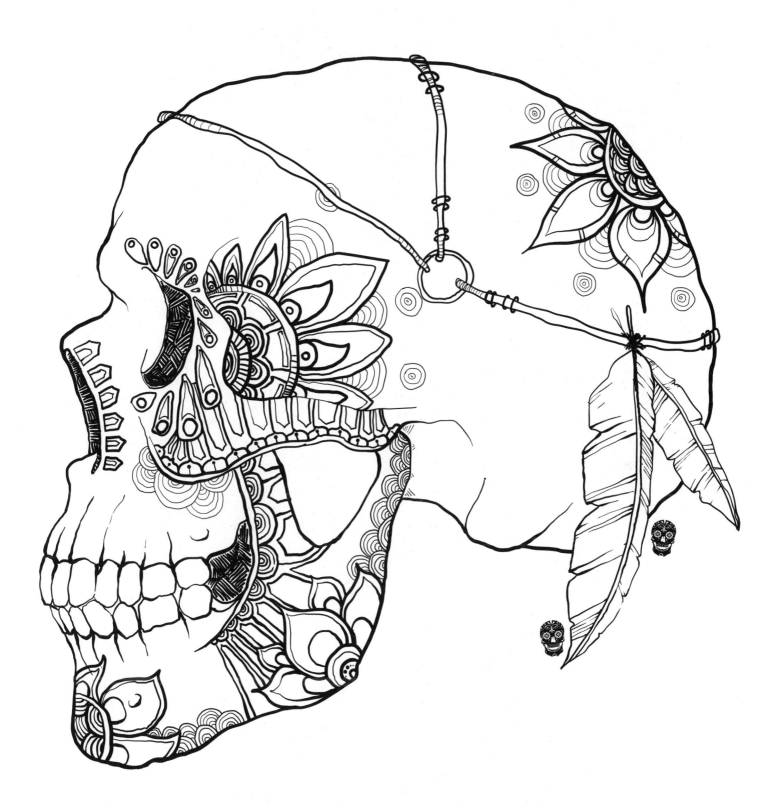